HOW I BECAME PRESIDENT
OF
THE UNITED STATES OF AMERICA

HOW I BECAME PRESIDENT
OF
THE UNITED STATES OF AMERICA

FORMER PRESIDENT STUART KIEHL

McCaa Books • Santa Rosa, CA

McCaa Books
1604 Deer Run
Santa Rosa, CA 95405-7535

ISBN 978-1-7358074-1-6
Library of Congress Control Number 2020918360

First published in 2020 by McCaa Books,
an imprint of McCaa Publications.

Printed in the United States of America
Set in Minion Pro

Cover Photo by Stuart Kiehl ©
Stuart Kiehl's Photo by Marcy Maloy ©

www.mccaabooks.com

Dedication

Judas and Benedict Arnold in the mix,
but Best in Show goes to Little Hands,
fleeing multiple arrest warrants,
now in Trump Tower Moscow

PROLOGUE

Steve Bannon

Michael Moore

Stuart Kiehl

We all agree on who could be the next President of the US.

I was the one who made it happen.

This is the story of how I became President of the United States, defeated Little Hands, and stopped the attack of five billion robo calls a month on Americans, taken from my informal notes before, during and after the ride to the White House. Efforts continue to stop political calls, now exempted.

Read on to see how the above three characters predicted an outcome determined by me.

I

The whole thing pretty much started on the first of April. April Fool's Day.

After a rum or two, the irony did not escape me, and I thought it was sort of appropriate. Little would I see the consequences then, but which everyone in the world now knows, I became President of the United States, POTUS.

My friends said, "I'll vote for you," and encouraged me to continue what then was in my mind a logical sequence of events for me occupying The White House.

There is one issue which unites every American. Democrats, Independents, and Republicans alike want to stop all robo and unsolicited calls.

And that was my one and only campaign issue.

I think I have lots of big ideas, but this one issue headed back to roost on our favorite joke day. That began some phone calls, URL searches, and requirements to be included on the Democratic debate stage. A friend once commented that I have a "very fertile mind," to which I agreed, not yet calling up the cerebral troops to weaponize this conversational remark.

I would run for President on a single "No Robo or Unsolicited Calls" campaign issue, people would agree and send me money to qualify for the Democratic debates, then the others would split the vote, and I would hold my own, do well in the early Iowa Caucuses, and New Hampshire and South Carolina primaries, build momentum and publicity, get the Democratic nomination and go on to beat Little Hands.

So my fertile mind imagined, but reality imposed.

A few hints on my thoughts of what you are reading. The tenses in this story, understood, are not consistent, maybe a tad confusing, and are the result of random notes on the way to and from The White House, oblique and slight stream of consciousness occasion the different time lines, but please stay onboard because none of this was expected to happen!

The first debate was two months away from when I began the thought process of this voyage. Holy Cow! No one knew of my candidacy and I was dreaming of occupying the White House. To be eligible for the Dem debates, a candidate needed 65,000 contributors, 200 of them in at least 20 states. The 20 on the stage would be the highest 20 vote getters based on contributors, or polling the highest.

Jump a few steps ahead, to follow my thinking. I'm still in the Big Picture mode, though I will return to qualifying for the debates.

In the last presidential election there were 17 Republican candidates. All except Little Hands were essentially clones. So he stood out. He also had his TV show audience and the National Inquirer crowd (the boss since indicted). So the 16 little chickens split the vote, too cowardly, then and now, to confront the guy insulting them, their wives and families.

They cringed, he kept getting his share of the votes and got the brass ring.

For the first Democratic debate, there would be 20 candidates with minor differences. And there will be one outlier, with only one single issue: stop all robo and unsolicited calls.

Sure, I said, why not? Why not me, saying vote for me because my single issue is to stop robo call attacks, and all Americans can agree to this as a start to unify the country again.

Overnight, the media would start the machine, while weirdo pulls a huge upset and wins, etc!

The free publicity would supercharge the message, talk show hosts would invite me and a few celebrities jokingly would say they would endorse me, so the public would become aware that the contest had indeed taken a new twist.

I would do well in the first few states, starting with Iowa, then gathering steam in New Hampshire with my challenge to all other candidates to join me in asking for a ban of all unsolicited calls, including political calls which are permitted in New Hampshire. Needless to say, the New Hampshire Democratic leadership was aghast, but the voters would agree with me.

The other candidates waffled on banning political calls, which would get me more votes.

Because I was not campaigning for any ethnic, economic, social group or cause, I hoped enthusiasm, curiosity and frustration for the weirdo would carry me to the general election, where I would face Little Hands, and win because more people simply wanted him gone and would take anyone else, especially a guy ranting about submitting a bill to Congress on his first day in office preventing unsolicited calls.

This was my thinking.

Guess what? I won.

II

My good friend, Mark, who encourages my sometimes flights of what I would call creativity, said a viral video was needed, and he sent me links of a million people watching someone take apart an iPhone.

His message: do a video which goes viral to get the 65,000 contributing viewers.

Okay, that would be a creative and practical challenge. Not addressing the message, content or production of the Viral Video, I started first with where do they send the donation after seeing the yet to be made video, and a pitch for a dollar to stop daily phone call attacks? A Federal Election Commission ID was required for ActBlue to collect the money. That required a separate bank account for the campaign. Phone, website and URLs were needed. Completing the basic mechanics were necessary before the video was aired, so if it become viral, the money would have a home for deposits from the video.

What would get 65K people to send in at least one dollar, to make the required 65K contributors? That would be one of my campaign pitches, One Dollar Donations Welcome! A Buck!

Everyone across America get a jar and put one penny a day into it. A Penny a Day!

And at the same time, I was thinking about the video itself, mostly what do I want to say? How to shoot it is no big deal to me as photography, film and video shooting has been one of my careers in New York, Los Angeles and Europe.

The Mission: make a video which will get 65K contributions, and gather 200 signatures in 20 states, the basic stage requirement.

Also the structural side of it was needed: donations collections, regulations, banking, etc.

I have done a lot of great images on film and video, including a President of the US, His Royal Highness Prince Philip, and my photos in *Vogue*. I have contributed ideas, and as a cameraman, generally I am shooting the scenes for others. As a photographer, the images, framing, lighting, etc. are mine. That's why I was hired, to support the client's visual needs, whether fashion, products, boats or concepts.

Now, this was my own production, I was the client, the screenwriter, producer, director, editor and cameraman. And investor and owner.

III

I am alone, my friends are frustrated with the political arena, them not having the time for what they consider a frivolous but amusing effort. This is not my job, but I feel that because no one is doing it, why the bleep not? Certainly, it would be more reasonable to run for some local office and completely understandable that folks would say this may be a bit of a high bar to stop an annoyance.

But the fact is I am doing it and plugging along. Got the bank acct, Stuart Kiehl for President, setting up the website, have the Federal Election Commission forms done, next is contacting the ActBlue people to receive money, choose a URL, make the video, then post it to YouTube and social media.

$25 has been spent so far to open a Stuart Kiehl for President bank account.

I am working on the website, looking for friends to help with the video, which will be key. The content and visuals will bring this campaign out of the shadows, so I am juggling a bunch of stuff alone, with the meter running for the debates.

This is not an ego thing, it is an attack, an intrusion and harassment which offends me and the entire country every day and night. Our duty, I feel, is to make things better that are unfair. These robocalls must be stopped.

IV

Meanwhile, the Federal Election Commission registration is complete and ActBlue is ready for any money. Of interest is what happens to any donations if I am not one of the 20 onstage, or hopefully, if I am?

Any funds collected can be used for campaigns or campaigning was the basic Federal Election Commission answer. A lot of mechanical requirements coming together, but the video is still the biggie.

I called the DNC, (does anyone work there?), and my question was what is the determination for stage presence after the basic 65K/200/20 qualifications are met, most money or most contributors?

Turns out contributors, because if it was dough, I'd lose. Some hedge fund douche could drop gobs, but if it is a number of people throwing in a buck, then the field is leveled a bit. Next, do a website with links to ActBlue and then do the video. Website will be simple. Video can make it. Or not.

V

I'm still solo, email set up, three-page website laid out by me. It needs to be activated with a deposit link.

GoFundMe will allow political campaigns, minimum $5 donation. ActBlue $1.

The elephant in the room is the video, and I think I have a good idea: use my iPhone to have public testimonials say they will vote for me for POTUS to stop robocalls.

This concept has a few things going for it: No big camera, crew, lights, reflectors, equipment, just me and my iPhone. Over many years I have heard more than a few times, "I'll break your lens if you film me," not that they will bust up the gear, but a self-disparaging remark about themselves.

Bottom line smaller camera is more relaxing for non professionals, and the iPhone concept has a lot going for it:

—Since the program is ALL Americans, it will work having the public BE the message

—Off the cuff comments better than a script

—Includes all shades, walks of life, activities, businesses, etc.

—No other good ideas so let's start with this.

I think it is the perfect format and content, emphasizing the grassroots part of the campaign, and using the words of Americans to express their feelings about my one issue presidential campaign.

What a hoot! Have shot a dozen iPhone enthusiastic short messages of support, one with Golden Gate Bridge in background from aboard a friend's boat on the SF Bay, a set of joggers, some funny remarks from students at the Junior College, another from an Assisted Living friend with a row of strollers behind him, a Latino couple, in English and Spanish, a few sweaty folks while working out, headbands, spandex, a farmer with cows in background, a cannabis grower with indoor weed plants, a wine grower in rows of grapes, my mechanic working on my car on the lift, and more….

"I'll vote for you!" is the common theme. The selfie with camera mount on a hang glider was a big hit, wind whipping by, big goggles, huge smile and thumbs up, "You got my vote!" Another one from up in the air was a friend in her plane, headphones on, can't hear her because of aircraft noise, but "I'll vote for you!" was pretty clearly understood.

On the To Do list is a pawn shop, western equestrian folk, assembly line workers, a CEO type with big panorama glass window background, a secretary, teacher with kids, a mom with kids, a stud of some type, ditto a babe, just some average folk, military and law enforcement types, hard hats, simply anyone and everyone.

On a trip to Sacramento, capitol of California which resembles the US Capitol, I got a bunch of groups already posing for photos on the big steps, to shout WE ALL AGREE and to then yell, "you have our permission to use this video," as a release. These group shots scored big time: enthusiastic and laughing 4H kids; a high school group; a Black choir group in maroon robes with big white collars sang " We All Agree" repeatedly, in their own beautiful melody, wow!

VI

You know what this is? It is a blueprint for some (other) weirdo to become POTUS, and because I succeeded and am now publishing the template, the public may get another oddball after me.

What concerns me is that someone with marketing expertise, and who can navigate, manipulate or meet the requirements to get to the stage, will overcome those with good intentions.

Little Hands did it with his TV show voters, lots of dough and his bestie, Vlad. He beat the conventional yappers. I did too with no TV show, money, support, organization, or the assistance of an adversarial foreign power.

If I could do it, others could as well, one can be a force for Good or Greed. If the Message Machines convince enough of The Passives, then there is a danger of the Unique Thinking becoming a tool of regression and suppression under the guise of "freedom," the standard far right and Putin puppets propaganda, aka fox, Little Hands TV.

VII

A lot more candidates have entered the race, big and little names. All in the group are fine by me, the stage will hold the only top 20 in two events. The qualifications are established: basic threshold requirements have to be met, and next is number of donors. Not the amount. Quantity trumps dough.

I'm thrilled to report successes with my iPhone recordings. The reactions of folks has been great, and when I say I am running for president on one issue, banning robo calls, nearly every person says "You've got my vote!"

Posting the most amusing, optimistic and mixed group of responses to YouTube with an appeal for a one dollar donation, (or more), and to send to ActBlue, the response has been overwhelming. Not necessarily unexpected because I am tapping into frustrations, AND offering a real solution. Somewhat like what Little

Hands did, without any solutions. And what the Ukraine President Zelenskiy achieved, he being a comedian.

The wild card is the Joker.

And it is happening in the US. People were frustrated and fed up in the last election, most did not like the Dem candidate and some actually believed in the lies of her opponent, leaving all but the moronic in utter frustration. Along I come, no political experience, no money, no supporters, but with a good idea of a solution to a problem the politicians have allowed to intrude into the privacy of every single person in this country.

Whamo! The floodgates open, the dam bursts, the heavens open, BANG! The money starts flowing in! And does not stop! In a very short time, I have reached my minimum required $65,000 and that is doubled soon after! Each single dollar donation counts as a contributor, so not only are the coffers filling up, the number of people donating is becoming very high.

Still solo, I'm now trying to figure out if I have the 200 donors in 20 states minimum required by the Democratic National Committee, DNC, and after some learning about how to configure the money donation system, the numbers confirm that I am eligible to be on the Democratic stage in June, hurray!

Now what? I call the DNC, (btw, get more operators, people!), and eventually get a call back from someone surprised by not knowing a candidate who now qualifies for the debates and whom she has never heard of, which starts a whole series of emails, confirmations, questions, etc., etc.

This is the turning point from me being just another guy with an idea and doing something about it to full bore media frenzy.

My name was on the list of debate stage candidates, and many known political figures, including current or ex mayors, governors, senators and members of congress, and billionaires did not make the cut.

Who is this guy?

I have one land line I never use and my cell phone. A friend's girlfriend is an accountant type of person, organized, knows spreadsheets, programs, etc., and I have been paying her to help with the ongoing flow of money, which continues to pile up, the average donation so far is around three bucks, most sending in a dollar or $5.00.

That is the entirety of The Campaign Staff at this stage.

But, I can't even use my phone anymore because it is always busy! I got a second cell phone, now I am carrying two phones, pretty tacky but necessary.

Am starting to feel like the movie stars always being hounded by the paparazzi.

Can't keep up with the emails, inquiries and invitations. One I accept because he is cool, Colbert, and they pay my way to NY to make the big announcement on his show. Rachel Maddow's people called, and they are covering expenses for an additional few nights to be on her show. Yippee, I think she is great.

One earlier skeptic, asked me if I was familiar with Veep? I asked what? "Veep." "What?" again.

"Veep," again. "What is it you are trying to say?" I inquired over the phone, my hearing is bad. I finally got that it was a TV show, which I have not seen, so any similarities or stealing ideas from the show do not exist. Ditto some recent movie about the presidency. But it did give me an idea, Rachel for my Veep! She's a lot smarter than me, and if I can get her in on my coattails, that would be a hoot.

Even more candidates are throwing their hats or bonnets in the ring, everyone coming out of the woodwork. "Novices abound on the campaign trail," a headline, "...presidential wannabes, some of whom have been in politics for 15 minutes and done little to establish their campaign or public policy bona fides....growing number of very junior hopefuls who apparently believe the only office that matters is the presidency ..."

Yes on the "novices". Nope on the "wannabes," I am the real thing.

"Very junior hopefuls," I do not even rate as very junior, that would be padding the resumé.

"Bona fides"? None. Except for my ideas. And action.

The point of this campaign was an annoyed citizen with a solution to a universal problem who became president. It is not unlike Little Hands before me, or the classy president before him. Who wudda thunk? Out of the ordinary, three in a row!

So, here we are, going down memory lane to an unexpected conclusion. Which I find not surprising. The people are mad, they are being invaded, the FCC is not protecting our basic privacy, the problem has gone beyond a Public Nuisance, it is a personal intrusion into our lives at all hours:

AMERICANS ARE BEING ATTACKED

And no one has, or is, doing anything to change this.

Forget words. I ask you, has it stopped, slowed down, about the same, or gotten worse? It is worse. You don't need me to tell you.

Every year it is worming into your personal space with increasing frequency, six million complaints last year! The FCC has now trotted our their "new bipartisan" policy, what a sham! Forget the claptrap. Forget the Do Not Call. Forget the new phony FCC ruse. Nothing has changed. And it won't.

Can you fight it? Yep, vote for me!

And that is why I became POTUS.

I was saying what everybody in the US felt, and they agreed with me.

The public gets it, and that is the reason that the videos of just normal people went viral and enabled me, us, to gain the qualification criteria for the Democratic debate stage.

Our numbers were staggering. I asked for a dollar donation, many contributed $5, so we went way beyond the $65,000 and 200 voters in at least 20 states.

My debate appearance will be Levi's, open neck white shirt and blue blazer, no tie. I hope to sound somewhat reasonable and offer a good presentation, on, literally, a pretty big stage. I do not know the name of the leader of Kurdistan, nor a bunch of other stuff, but what I do know is I do not want anyone calling me all day and night invading my privacy. That is my one and only campaign issue and I think if I can express that somewhat clearly, people will get it and either say, give it a shot, yeah, I like his message, or go for any other the other candidates, that is fine too.

The DNC stated the 20 "finalists" for the debate stage were based on the number of contributors over polling numbers and money, neither of which I had.

How could I qualify with polling? Would not happen, no one knows me, "...Stuart who..?" Ditto money, a hedge fund zillionaire could drop a billion and not even feel it.

But the wild card was the number of contributors, my campaign jumping over a bunch of other candidates because of the videos. I had more supporters than them! This loophole will be closed I am sure to prevent other wild card candidacies, but it was too late for my run. I was in. DNC rules required me to be allowed on stage.

Obviously, I was the odd man out, no excuse for the expression, it fits, so I'll use it. I am a man. I am odd. I am out of the norm.

And, you know what, because I do or did not pretend to be anyone I am not, people simply liked that. It was refreshing, and my message they could understand-that I was offering a reasonable solution: elect me on one thing we can agree on, and nail that down immediately, and then move on next to other national and international issues, and fix the compromised national security.

In a very short time, stringent, enforceable laws would be passed with severe penalties for those creating the problem, and those permitting it! Pass this legislation first, then address the other issues with a bipartisan success as a start.

The public understands their home invasion is being permitted by their government. We also get that Big Money is involved and the little guy is us, the American Public, which doesn't have much clout these days, especially on what is considered not a 'major issue'.

But, it IS a major issue when our homes are attacked continuously and our cell phones have been taken over by bandits, Congress being complicit. Don't tell me they can't do anything to stop this.

Back to the story, understood, I am jumping around, but I am not a writer or a politician. I am now President!

Hopefully, no one else will do what I did. Unless they will do good. But most of those people are killed or die in plane crashes. Why do the heathens win?

Why didn't anyone stop Hitler, Stalin or Little Hands? People are sheep. Ghandi is on the other side, but not many on the good side attain power.

Hand wringing "we done good" Dem concession speeches don't cut it. Power does.

Ask Moscow Mitch and look at the Supreme Court.

VIII

Debates are a media frenzy. I am on the first night, June 26 in Miami! No one knows how to contact me because I have no campaign staff or headquarters and do not answer my phone, but I will be on the stage. I have been staying on my boat in Sausalito, while those outside my house with the locked driveway gate and a "Beware of Dog" sign attached will have a long wait.

Being essentially the only Unknown of the 20, I was swamped with appearance invites and interviews. I took as many as possible. Colbert was funny and made me feel relaxed because he is so weird in his own way, the show went well and donations skyrocketed.

Rachel Maddow had me on and my compliments to her were effusive, but she lightly cut me off and asked about larger issues than stopping robo calls, which I refused to discuss, reminding her of my one issue. She was polite, courteous, informed and doing her job. We did have a few martinis after the show, her gin, me vodka, and she was what I pretty much expected, a real woman, very funny, loose, curious, learned and charming. After the second martini I offered her Veep for her endorsement and she cracked up.

The most interesting person of the 20 is me. All the others are rich or well known, I am neither. Understandable, so I am making all the decisions myself, no staff, no dough.

The actual debates were a success for a few reasons. I was different than them all.

My one message was understood by everyone in the audience and the tens of millions of viewers who wanted a solution.

They got the concept of let's together make a difference in our lives and complete one step as a start. Then move to the next.

This simple reasoning was expressed by me clearly, and I defended my participation on stage as a campaign from the bottom up, one person, frustrated and trying to do something about it.

I was pretty much ignored by the other candidates, but someone's indirect snide "one issue candidates" comment left me an opening, and I stormed though it, turning to Bernie, I smiled and said "...Bernie, last time you ran for president I supported you, I sent you money. Your average donation was $27, well, Bernie, now my campaign has done you one better. The American public has put me on this stage, I have more contributors than a bunch of senators who did not qualify, and my average donation is about three bucks! I am here on this stage, and not going away!"

My next opportunity was when I asked all the other candidates if they would raise their hands to ban political robo calls.

No one did.

Looking into the camera I said, "I am the only candidate in any party offering Americans privacy form political or commercial attacks. WE ALL AGREE. VOTE FOR ME!" The audience erupted.

That was another turning point.

Essentially, I had won the debates. From that point onward, it became a blur and the big stuff started, financial, mechanical, logistical, economic and technical. There was no confusion, people got it, headlines quoted, WE ALL AGREE, VOTE FOR ME.

IX

Thus started our campaign in Iowa, of which every other candidate was jealous, envious, perplexed and behind the times, the first contest for votes and delegates. Besides the weather, the challenge was I had no idea what to do, who to call or how to do it. I had no staff, and realized I needed others to answer the phones, drive and do all the other basic stuff of just getting from one place to another on time and knowing where to go next and how to get there.

The debates gave me a reluctant sense of credibility with the media, the other candidates continued to ignore me, which was fine, nor did I hammer them. I was not a concern to anybody.

I called a press conference in Iowa on the steps of the Capitol in the snow, a bunch of TV and print journalists attended, including some national programs looking for something different than the predictable speeches of all the other candidates. The crowd enthusiasm and visuals of the swirling snow were practically tactile when seen on TV.

I had rented a small store, it had a few desks and that was about it. I gave the address of my campaign "headquarters" during my speech and asked for volunteers to bring desks, chairs, computers and good humor. The next day the place was packed with young, old, Democrats, republicans, Independents, etc. Quickly, I quieted everyone down and asked if anyone in the room that had campaign organizing experience to see me at the back desk. The others I asked to write down what they thought would be needed to get the message out in Iowa and how they could help.

Dan had run local campaigns and seemed to know the ropes and I appointed him Iowa Campaign Manager. I appointed Sally to be Social Media Organizer. Then, I needed a few other positions, the first to get some phones and desks, the physical office needs. Also, a driver. And a Media Coordinator.

My long time friend Mark had to stay in California but was in the loop on computer/ media/

technical things, mostly the Big Picture stuff, the Grand Thinking, the suggester of The Viral Video.

All this took about a week, we got off the ground, big banners out front and inside, WE ALL AGREE. Websites were created, phones installed, etc..

This was the start of presenting a new message to all the Iowa voters.The difference between the other candidates and me, and which continued throughout the rest of the campaign and through the general election, was that I could, and did, go to any and all organizations and groups. This was a big difference between singing to the choir and a few otherwise curious, I was burrowing in areas where no politician dared appear because the political ilk was not the color of their party.

I then added a Production Director title and staff member, Elisa from the Film Studies at the university, whom I assigned the task of posting ten daily video responses to the campaign question. "..will you vote Stuart Kiehl for President if he stops robo calls?" She got her fellow students and friends to participate, and to post to their own sites as well. And to ask others to do the same.

This developed into a daily and increased media presence without paying a single penny for advertising. More importantly, these independent freelance support videos unexpectedly became possibly the most important marketing tool of the campaign, as each small cluster essentially became a mini campaign testimonial with extended social media legs.

Everyone was asked to make and post at least one video of support on their own social media platforms, and ask all friends to do the same with the question "will you support Stuart Kiehl for President if he stops robo calls, including political calls?"

This was outside of our "official" videos, this was all their own, the testimonials from their own surroundings. This concept scored beyond Viral. It was Stratosphere!

The self replicating aspect was beyond my expectations.

Every day more and more mini endorsements appeared everywhere, but not on billboards, advertising or the radio!

Oops, one exception, a billboard. Because we encouraged everyone to do their own thing, to make their own videos, one group in Oklahoma raised enough money for a highway sign with WE ALL AGREE screaming out from the background fluorescent green color of the vests of the traffic guys. BTW, one of the daily videos was a group of road workers in the bright green/yellow safety vests, hooting and hollering, one guy holding an orange cone on his head doing a little dance, revolving flashing light on truck, that got a big number of 'likes'.

I promised voters they would not see one single TV ad from me or get one single robo call from me, and to think of our campaign every time they saw or heard a TV or radio political commercial, or got a robo call from any candidate, reinforcing continuously to vote for me. "Every time you hear or see them without your permission, think of us. And vote for America", turning an invasion of their privacy into a reminder of the one candidate who was not attacking them!

I came in seventh in Iowa out of over twenty candidates.

That was essentially a political earthquake, and a mild surprise to us...

In New Hampshire, we used many of the same people and having learned a few ropes, we had contributions in the bank from the appearances, exposure and very respectable Iowa showing. This was easier and harder because we sorta thought we knew what was needed to set up shop, but the entire atmosphere was different because of our Iowa win. We were no longer an oddball campaign, but a potential threat to others, the party, and down the road, possibly a vote diversion costing the presidency to Little Hands, as the Green Party had done in two republican presidential " victories".

So, the tone changed from happy go lucky to a bit more serious, with the potential consequences being considered. With the Iowa "win", local and national media, and our social media daily blitz gaining more followers every day, each a mini advertising agency, we became known fast. Our contributions were off the charts, requiring additional staff.

The "video interviews" on social media by our followers were simple—an iPhone was held up and the question was asked "Will you vote for Stuart Kiehl for President, whose only issue is to stop robo and unsolicited calls, including political calls?"

After signing a release, or so stating on camera, ten answers from all types of everyday folk were posted daily, the enthusiasm, humor and sincerity understood and supported by all the viewers. At the end of each daily posting we pitched for a buck, or more.

The money was rolling in.

This was our "Official" posting, but what expanded beyond any expectations was our continual request for everyone to do their own posting, asking the same question, and requesting those viewing to do the same. It had already started in Iowa, and now took off on its own, we loved it, bottom up, real democracy!

Everything changed, again, after we came in third in NH. This train was now rumbling down the track, gathering speed and momentum.

This was now the top floor, top shelf, top tier etc, this was big time. And we were small time.

The ActBlue account collected the increasing amount of money which supported our budget campaign, the expenses being mostly travel, accommodations, salaries and rental of campaign offices in a few states.

The staff now included a South Carolina organizer and also a Nevada team member. These were the first early states in which to establish national credibility.

At this point, I realized a Chief of Staff was needed, someone who could absorb all the issues and figure out how to delegate or share with me, and the person who accepted this was "Birdlegs", a California longboard surfer who had helped start the Surfrider Foundation, had worked in the White House, produced and directed a documentary on a Republican Marine Congressman, author of "Surfer in the White House" and who had a great smile, talent and good cheer...

Everyone now wanted a piece of the action, and I was on the talk shows, including a second appearance on Colbert, all audience successes.

Next was a CNN Town Hall request, but I declined because an hour of questions and answers would probably have gotten me in trouble. We agreed to a 30 min segment with Anderson Cooper, who was, as always, courteous but curious in a wry manner.

I gave my spiel, blah, blah, took questions from the audience, then turned the tables on them and the hosts. I got out of my chair, walked to the front of the stage, and said to the crowd, a pause before I spoke quietly "..now, I have a question for you…..", long pause, then louder ,"…..all those who want to stop robo and unsolicited and political calls, please stand up!" Nearly the entire audience stood up, and those seated could not be seen because of the people standing, so not only was it a real endorsement, the visuals from TV made it seem every person in the place supported me.

My question to the audience became news in itself, further giving the campaign more free publicity. And emphasizing with every appearance that not a single dollar was being spent on negative advertising. Or positive advertising. Or any advertising. Or polling. Or opposition research. Or meeting with Russians.

So all the contributors felt their money was actually going into bread and butter needs for a campaign for them! And it was.

Meanwhile, the social media campaign of ten daily interviews continued with increasing success, including some big names we would occasionally cross paths with now that we were mixing with The Upper Percentile, and with official encouragement, the expanding numbers of supporters did their own very impactful "mini testimonials" postings.

All staff members were assigned to ask The Question to anyone, interesting or not. And to have them give verbal permission after the iPhone query.

This bottom up campaign, outside of our control, became the spine of the campaign-the American people using the new tools available to them without realizing their own power until they dipped their toe in the water! The Russians attacked the US, the republican party is now complicit with a foreign hostile adversary, but the American people now had the potential to match the informational powers of the former Soviet Union and KGB, GRU, NBC, CBS, ABC, CNN, and fox!

This resulted in a further media expansion of the campaign and became a bit of a cult, waiting for the new daily testimonials. We started to spice up the production values, continuously being sharpened with humor, graphics, music and a feeling of optimism and closing with a pitch for a dollar or more donation.

While this was the "official" daily posting, the thousands of other supporters provided more exposure than our own efforts, furthering the message, voter registration, delegates and financial support.

New statewide URLs had to be obtained, websites made and maintained, these were some of the other required issues, but we had the money to do it so we found some good people and had a basic program set up, hired as needed, either as staff, or for specific statewide purposes, or both.

Then fox invited me and I accepted. They hammered me with what I had written and published over the last decade, all available to anyone, none of which I denied, discussed or retracted—that the republican party today is the most dangerous organization in the world, trump is Putin's bitch, voting machines are hackable, and other stuff, but I not would discuss any of that though the host persisted. I equally resisted, saying my campaign is one issue only: ".. to stop robo and unsolicited calls to Americans. Including political calls.." They requested, and I agreed, to not ask the audience to stand up.

However, no mention was made of asking the audience for a show of hands if they would support a candidate who would stop the invasion of their privacy by companies and politicians.

So, that's what I did, I asked for a show of hands. Whamo! It seemed like everyone held their hand up, the fox moderator, caught off guard, cut to a commercial and then returned the discussion to my single issue. Another free

TV marketing bonanza, as this became itself a news story once more.

In South Carolina, I decided to cover bases in both the white and black communities, telling of my experiences in the state and some family history. These apparent contradictions were starkly stated in editorials and by other candidates, saying he can't have it both ways. But I could and I did. Here's the deal.

My middle name is Lee. My aunt, Georgia Lee, was part of the Daughters of the American Confederacy, and supposedly I had a relative with Lee at Appomattox. None of that was my doing or me naming myself. But it did have an appeal to a segment I did not court.

The other side was the black community, and I shared a story of my first year in college, at the University of South Carolina, where I danced with a black girl at the first dance.

Turns out it was the first year of integrating the school. Anyway, I get called in to the Dean of Students Office and was told I would be watched "..in class and out of class, we don't want any out-siders, martyrs or crusaders here…"

WTF????

I had no idea what kind of place this was and I transferred as soon as I could to George Washington University.

A numbers of things, individually or collectively, appealed to voters:

—The main message: Stop robo and unsolicited calls. And that it could be accomplished. This was big, as it transcended party, cultural, gender, economic, ethnic or any other categories.

—And to stop POLITICAL calls without permission. I was the only one saying this at every chance. And, asking the public to ask the other candidates if they would agree. No other candidate agreed, this helped me, so I kept using it to separate myself from the pack.

—As part of my pitch, I repeatedly said no negative ads. No positive ads. No ads at all. I asked all audiences to think of our campaign every time they saw a political ad on TV or got a political call invading their privacy.

—Dollar, or more, donations. This was historic and a game changer. Voters loved it. Most sent more, and many gave more than once. I pointed this out all the time.

—"A Penny A Day" push was throwing stuff against the wall and see if it would stick. This was another surprisingly lucrative concept.

—Our social media marketing was entirely the American people. Period. Their words and images recorded on an iPhone and uploaded every day. Our daily "WE b4 them", ten testimonials became a viral event every day. And the ever expanding "non official" social media testimonials from our supporters on their own was simply brilliant, free and self generating. And bringing in money!

—I was completely different from all the rest. I was not a politician. I was not a lawyer. I was not an elected official or had been. I was sort of your Average Joe, an outsider fed up, and wanted to do something about being attacked day and night. And...

I had a solution.

This was huge. So often people whine or complain, but what can or will they do about it?

Vote for me, which is vote for the American people, and we will stop this privacy invasion with legislation on my first day in office. I was offering a real solution.

Because no one else recognized the depth of the frustration, our campaign now had legitimacy. The public believing THEY could participate in stopping an attack on them with a real solution was the key.

We came in fourth in South Carolina. Yes, an excellent showing. And, we were accumulating delegates. And recognition nationwide.

More primaries, more delegates, more exposure, more money kept coming. With success over well known names of politics or finance, I was still the wild card. I continued to refuse, for the most part, to discuss impeachment, or Little Hands or any other issue: Stop robo, unsolicited and political calls unless permission given.

We learned more of the mechanics of moving from state to state, but the message was consistent and simple. Because of this, we were racking up delegate numbers and the publicity was gigantic, further adding to the momentum.

Super Tuesday and the other primaries were hectic and confusing, and we missed a few state deadlines to be included on the ballot, we just did not have the horsepower to have a presence everywhere, but I did visit those states, sometimes a few in one day, and asked all audiences to spread the word as a write in candidate.

By this time we had our own chartered plane, a twin engine Bonanza, WE ALL AGREE on each side, owned by a volunteer ex Navy pilot who flew for expenses, fuel, food and lodging, a good guy whom we trotted out at times wearing his wings and uniform when we talked to veteran's groups. Me having an Honorable Discharge opened doors and I sometimes strayed off topic, ridiculing Little Hands, him being in Japan for Memorial Day and hiding the Navy Cruiser John McCain during the visit. How can any veteran vote for this guy? Calling them "suckers" and "losers." Where is Honor and Duty?

These remarks were made at an American Legion Hall, I could not resist, and got a rousing enthusiast standing ovation from the guys and gals.

X

Going into the Dem convention, I was third in delegates. The first two candidates were beginning to claw at each other, their personal agendas interfering with what I and others considered the greater good, so while they were scraping at each other, I called the next few folks down from me and suggested a meeting.

51% of the delegates was needed for victory, and the two ahead of me could have combined, but bad blood was developing, so the meeting of me in third place and the next three below combined for what could be the nomination.

New territory for all, we spent a few nights hashing things out, a lot of back and forth, the ultimate goal was to make one of us POTUS, combining delegates to reach 51%. I was next in line, so obviously I was tooting my own horn.

Why would the three conventional candidates combine with "robo guy" and not support either of the top two party line candidates?

A few reasons, the first was during the campaign, things had been said and done to them by the top two in the heat of running for office. Sometimes directly, other times more subtle, but slights nevertheless, so it was personal, whether justified or not.

Second, it was felt that the top two should put country before their candidacies and combine as POTUS and VP. They refused.

This is why Rubio is now senator, two Florida Democrats split the vote and Rubio walked in. Ego before ethics. Circular firing squad of Democrats.

Most importantly was my VP choice.

Michelle Obama as Vice President.

She felt that at this time, in her life and that of the country, she could devote the required energy to restoring trust in a system which had been sabotaged by both internal and external enemies, and that because her children were young adults, she wanted a better country for them.

During the meetings and discussions, I agreed that if we won, I would call in a Notary Public, and resign under the 25th Amendment and Ms. Obama would become the first woman President and could then appoint her own Veep, either from the candidates below me in delegates, or anyone else, including her husband, or his vice president, now with the most delegates.

She could become POTUS and not even have run for the office or won or earned a single delegate.

She indicated she would want her husband's Veep, but that was down the road, we first had to win the nomination and then the General Election.

As POTUS, she could appoint important Cabinet positions or Ambassadorships to the three candidates behind me in delegates if they wished to change jobs.

We won the nomination.

Mostly, this journey has been one of surprises and a newly found confidence in the American public, but that was only from OUR political and practical perspective, what was most revealing to everyone, every single citizen, was the realization that THEY HAD THE POWER to change things! This new found confidence and encouragement rebuilt the shattered trust in the systems.

"We the People" are the first three words in our Constitution, often forgotten.

Michelle mostly went to the big states, I went to the small and red states, where people understood they had been played by Little Hands.

Michelle destroyed Pence in her debate, him robot like, ramrod stiff, fake smile vs her charm, love, power, knowledge, and a spine of steel. It was no contest.

My "debates" with Little Hands were Janus faced theater, sadness and humor, of which he did not appreciate and wailed like a baby every time I addressed him as "Little Hands", him asking that the office of the Presidency be respected.

I replied, "Mr. Little Hands, when you qualify for the office, I will address you as such." Little Hands tried name calling me "Mr Robo Dodo," to which I laughed and asked him, "Mr. Little Hands, have you done one thing that has not benefited Putin? Have you done one thing to benefit the American people over your crime family and cronies?" He erupted, using his standard Blame Hillary and Fake News lines, with no reaction from me. I smiled at him. He scowled.

His next move was the historic game changer, he tried his "hovering" technique again during our first debate, slinking over to my space behind me, and I turned to him and said, "Little Hands, if you want to be close to me, let's meet in a boxing ring for our next debate, with or without gloves, and last man standing wins. Yes or no? Otherwise please return to your trough"

I turned back to the audience, dismissing him.

He exited back to his side, muttering.

This was mano-o-mano. This was core. You or me, buddy. He blinked. He caved.

That scene was the election.

No one has or had challenged Little Hands. They all backed down from The Fight. Until then. Voters want strength, not weakness. Democrats still do not get that.

We won the election, both in electoral and popular votes, not close, no calls for recounts anywhere. It was a landslide.

My first words at the inauguration were " We made America Great Again!" the oath administered by the Chief Justice.

I could not turn to Little Hands because he was in Mar a Lago. He had snuck out at night on Marine One, the presidential helicopter. Good riddance.

I resigned two days after being inaugurated, just had to spend a few nights in the White House, and hoped to become a writer and consultant for political campaigns.

25th Amendment, notary public, I resign, Veep takes over.

This transfer of power was legal and is still not well known. Congress did not and could not interfere. We did it quietly and successfully, lots of consternation but bottom line it was a permitted process.

The new POTUS, Madame President, first time ever said in this country, offered the Veep position to her husband's VP, three unsuccessful presidential campaigns, and him somewhat insulted by being beaten by "the robo guy." He declined.

Power to the People. Over and out.

EPILOGUE

Little Hands did not exit gracefully, whining and being a cry baby, but most Americans finally saw him for what he was, a coward, a fraud and a bully. Out of courtesy, with a straight face, but not seriously, one of my first acts during those two days, was to offer him the Ambassador position to either Mexico or Russia. He ranted his refusal in his normal 140 character method. By this time I was reluctantly on that social platform and shared a photo of him half way down the escalator, writing #bybyputinsbitch "down, down, down. and now out. loser. c u."

In those two days in office, I appointed Sally Yates as Attorney General, and Andrew McCabe as FBI Director, General Wesley Clark as Secretary of Defense, and a former CIA Director, and other former professionals from the intelligence agencies to restore our compromised national security. The VP agreed to these appointments and the rest would be up to her.

I pardoned all those in any state for marijuana convictions, and wanted to do a lot more, but I stayed two days in the White House and then resigned.

Our government finally took action on stopping robo calls. They had to.

In my inaugural speech I asked every elected official in the country, including all members of the Senate and Congress to pass legislation prohibiting any unsolicited calls without permission, and to vote out anyone not doing so. It took a while to get the wording right, and the legislation was passed soon after I had resigned. States and localities passed similar legislation.

But the prohibition on political robo calls was not passed.

Indictments in the US were issued for the CEOs of the offending robo call organizations. Abroad, Interpol got involved, searching for the heads of foreign violators, meaning they could not travel far from their home countries without being arrested. Any American employee from the attacking companies was offered a job in my newly created cabinet post, Department of Security.

Me? Many offers from campaigns and K Street lobbying firms, but I decided to do my consulting from a non fluorescent lighted office. The campaign money raised and now a substantial figure, still being added to every day, and collecting interest, was distributed to various candidates and programs devoted to voter registration, paper ballots and hand counting. Federal law permits these unused funds for campaigning, so after contributions to people and causes, what better way to continue the message of banning political robo calls than aboard a boat:

Even Kiehl for President is on the transom of three vessels, East and West coasts and Europe, campaigning and consulting for good causes.

The campaign issues have now doubled.

—Stop political robo calls.

—Eliminate the Electoral College. One person one vote. Most votes win.

The "penny a day" slogan created a shortage of pennies, as millions continued to collect and send in about three dollars every year, times millions of people it was substantial.

For good or bad I don't know, but the penny has since been eliminated in US currency.

The viral videos have become mainstream and are now their own program, which is based mostly on viewer contributions without fear of advertising dollars diluting the message. The movement in social media has created and awakened the entire country, empowering them with newfound enthusiasm in the process of democracy. The continual funds contributed, mostly single digit, keep and make this new channel thrive and expand.

From Tiananmen Square, The Arab Spring in Tunisia to now, the average person in the world wants pretty much the same thing, the tools have been, and will be, used to pervert, prevent, control and misinform the viewers-see fox. We are changing that for the benefit of positive causes, and staying vigilant in defense of continuing cyber attacks. It is a constant struggle, but we showed it could be done for a good purpose.

Another spinoff was the new online program gathering steam "fox LIES", hosted by former fox "newscasters", personalities and many well known conservatives disgusted by the hate and lies of this network.

Republicans know the tools of attack, unlike the Dems, so this has been an effective collaboration with The Lincoln Project, former republicans turned against the propaganda machine of fox and Putin.

fox is never capitalized, a subtle demeaning any time the word appeared. We started that effort and is now used regularly by many. fox audience numbers are declining.

These outlets are messages of hope. Yes, Obama, you were right, it is a powerful word, leading to action and change.

Steve Bannon, Michael Moore and I understood and agreed that Madam President Obama could become a reality.

The New Yorker, *The Atlantic* and the *New York Times Magazine* all wanted first publication rights. After its magazine publication, a book deal was arranged, speaking tour, appearances again with now familiar faces, and the *New York Times* had the book on its Bestseller list after first publication by a local boutique firm, McCaa Books.

Under Fiction.

About the Author

Stuart Kiehl has written articles on Russian hacking attacks, voting machines, NRA, Republicans, Democrats, Women's March, Sports in San Francisco and strategy and actions for change. He has lived, worked and played around the world, sailed the entire Pacific Coast from Canada to Cabo, was a fashion photographer in NYC and cinematographer on films and videos in LA, Honorable Discharge, Top Secret clearance, United States Coast Guard 100 GT Master, captain and owner of a Sausalito berthed charter boat, and now lives in Washington on a bluff overlooking the Straits of Juan de Fuca and night lights of Victoria.